Jenny Valentine

Iggy & Me

Illustrated by Joe Berger

HarperCollins *Children's Books*

First published in Great Britain by HarperCollins
Children's Books in 2009
HarperCollins *Children's Books* is a division of
HarperCollins *Publishers* Ltd
77-85 Fulham Palace Road, Hammersmith, London W6 8JB

www.harpercollins.co.uk

3

Text copyright © Jenny Valentine 2009
Illustrations © Joe Berger 2009

Jenny Valentine and Joe Berger assert the moral right to be
identified as the author and the illustrator of this work.

ISBN: 978-0-00-728362 0

Mixed Sources
Product group from well-managed
forests and other controlled sources
www.fsc.org Cert no. SW-COC-1806
© 1996 Forest Stewardship Council
FSC

FSC is a non-profit international organisation established to promote the
responsible management of the world's forests. Products carrying the FSC
label are independently certified to assure consumers that they come
from forests that are managed to meet the social, economic and
ecological needs of present and future generations.

Find out more about HarperCollins and the environment at
www.harpercollins.co.uk/green

Contents

Iggy and me

My name is Flo and I have a little sister. When she was even smaller than she is now, my little sister changed her name. One morning she woke up and she just wasn't called it any more.

It was very confusing.

We were sitting up in my bed making snowflakes. She woke me up early to make them. My sister often comes into my bed in the mornings, before I am quite ready for good

news or making things. There were tiny bits
of paper all over the sheets and the floor.

That's how she got
me to sit up, by
sprinkling them on
my face. My sister
had only just got
good with scissors
and she found it
very exciting.

We were supposed to make snowflakes out of old magazines, because we're not allowed to use new paper for stuff unless we have a very good reason, like a birthday or a sorry or a thank you letter. Snowflakes were not a very good reason and even though I told my sister that more than twice, she was using new paper because she so wanted them to be pure, bright white with no writing on them.

"Look at mine," she said, holding up snowflake number twenty-seven.

"Very good," I said. "Can I have the scissors now?"

"I'm using them," she said.

"You're not."

"I am in a minute."

"Sam," I said, because that was my sister's name. "You have to share."

"My name's not Sam," she said.

I didn't say anything, because I thought it was just her annoying way of not sharing. I didn't realise she was serious. And I had to wait ages for the scissors.

Later, we were all in the kitchen in our pyjamas. On not-school days we always eat breakfast with pyjamas on, sometimes even lunch. Mum and Dad look funny in their pyjamas in the mornings, all creased and sort of puffy. Mum's hair was wild and frizzy, and Dad's stuck out more on one side than the

10

other. And they had no slippers on even though they are *always* telling us to wear ours.

My sister had stuck all her white snowflakes on to the fridge until it looked like it was wearing a wedding dress. Every time you opened the fridge door, the snowflakes fluttered in the breeze like lace.

I said, "The fridge is getting married."

My sister said, "To who? To Daddy?" and laughed at her own joke like crazy. She loves her own jokes.

"Sam," Mum said. "Toast or cereal?" My sister didn't answer.

"Sam," Mum said. "Hello? Earth calling Sam!"

She still didn't answer. She turned her face away and her forehead went all smooth, like it does when she's pretending not to hear you.

"Sam," Mum said again. "What do you want for breakfast?"

Nothing. Not a peep.

"Sammy," said Dad, putting his arm round the fridge and kissing it. "Mum is talking to you."

"No she's not," said my sister, and then she pointed at him and laughed. "Mr and Mrs Fridge."

"She is," Dad said. "You heard her. We all did."

"She's not talking to me," my sister said. "She's talking to *Sam*."

Nobody said anything for a minute. It was very quiet in the kitchen. I could hear the kettle bubbling and my cereal landing on itself in my bowl. I looked at Mum, and Mum looked at Dad, and we all looked at my sister. She still looked like Sam to me, twiddling her hair and wearing her pyjamas with the fairies on.

"We thought *you* were Sam," said Mum.

My sister looked behind her, both sides, as if Mum was talking to someone there. "Who, *me?*" she said, "Who, ME?" Like we were the dumbest people on Earth.

"Yes, you," Mum said.

"I'm not Sam," my sister said, all matter-of-factly. "There's no one here called that name at all."

Dad started looking under the table and in the cereal boxes and in the bin. "There's a Sam around here somewhere," he said. "I know she was here a minute ago." He made a big show of it, checking in his armpits, looking in her hair like a monkey at the zoo, calling, "Sa-am, Sa-am!"

My sister giggled. "She's not here," she said. "Sam's not here."

Mum said that there used to be a little girl in the family called Sam. She said, "I'll be a little tiny bit annoyed if somebody has gone and lost Sam because I was starting to quite like her, thank you very much."

My sister shrugged. She said, "I don't know where she is."

"So who are you?" Dad said.

And I said, "What's your name?"

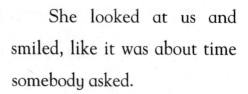

She looked at us and smiled, like it was about time somebody asked.

"My name's called Iggy," she said. She looked so proud of herself that she made me think of a peacock with its tail all fanned out behind.

Mum laughed and my little sister told her not to, so she pretended to drink her tea instead, but I could see she was still smiling. Dad said Iggy sounded like a piglet, or a puppet of a piglet, or a knitted egg-cup with a piglet's nose.

"Or a girl," my sister said, and she frowned at him. "Because it's my name and I am one."

"What, a piglet?" said Dad.

"No, silly, a *girl*."

"It doesn't sound like the one we bought," Mum said. "The little girl we bought was *definitely* a Sam."

My sister shook her head and pointed at herself and said, "Well, this one is *defilately* an *Iggy*."

"I like it," I said. "It suits you."

My sister said, "Good," and then, "Of course it suits me, it's my name." Then she said, "You didn't buy me really, anyway, did you?"

My cereal spluttered when I poured the milk on it. My sister said, "Please can I have some?" so I passed her a bowl and a spoon and the box and the milk, and she said, "Thank you, Flo."

I looked behind me, both sides, and I said, "There's no one called Flo around here." I was just joking.

Mum and Dad's mouths opened and laughed, but my sister's mouth stayed all closed and deadly serious. She was not pleased.

After that we didn't want her to be cross, because when my sister gets cross, she can be very boring and we all have to listen. So we played the Iggy game all breakfast to avoid it.

We said, "Pass the butter please, Iggy" and "Drink your juice, Iggy" and "Stop kicking me, Iggy" and "Put your chin over the bowl, Iggy" and "Ow, Iggy!" and "Iggy, behave!"

In fact, we played it all day because we thought that maybe if we said Iggy enough, she would get tired of it and want to change back. That was the idea anyway.

When we were getting dressed, I remembered to call her Iggy.

When she refused to help me tidy up the snowflakes on my bed, I called her Iggy, even though she was annoying me and I might easily have forgotten.

When she asked me to do her name in bubble writing on a sign for her door, I remembered to write Iggy so I didn't have to do it again.

Mum and Dad remembered to use her new name too. They said, "Iggy this" and "Iggy that."

They said, "Iggy, eat your lunch by half past or there's no pudding."

They said, "Iggy, don't cheat at Snap."

They said, "Iggy, when did you last clean your teeth?"

They said, "Iggy, Flo is trying to read. Stop jumping up and down on the sofa."

Even when my sister came down from her room with a box, we didn't say anything. In the box she'd packed all the things she could find with SAM written on them. Socks and

pencils and a plastic cup and a key ring and
some Post-it notes and a green teddy bear and
a purse, and a tiny car licence plate from
California that our Auntie Kate had sent her,
and a painting that I did when she was born,
that said her name in my
writing, before I was very
good at doing it. My sister
loved that painting.

"This is for Sam," she said.

Dad said, "Where do you want me to put it, Iggy?"

My sister shrugged, "In the rubbish."

Mum said, "Don't you think Sam will come back for it?"

My sister shook her head. "Nuh-uh," she said. "No way."

I said, "I thought you liked that painting."

She said, "I do. Can you do another one for Iggy?" And I said I would.

My mum and dad put the box in the cupboard under the stairs when she wasn't looking, just in case. And they said, "Goodnight, Iggy."

And, "Sleep tight, Iggy."

And, "Mind the bugs don't bite, Iggy."

And I said, "See you in the morning, Iggy. We can make more snowflakes."

We didn't go wrong at all. We thought we were being so clever. We nudged each other and winked at each other all day long.

When we woke up next morning we said, "Is Sam back yet?"

My sister said, "Nope."

And the morning after that she said, "Nope."

And the morning after that she said, "Who's Sam?"

We soon worked out who was in charge. It

was definitely Iggy. Because Iggy's her name and it's been her name since the morning she said so. The Iggy game turned into something real and after a while we all got used to it.

Iggy has a new plastic cup and some pencils with her name on, but no key ring yet or Post-its, and definitely no licence plate from California. Mum sewed IGGY on to a teddy and I did a new painting for her which was much, much better than the first one.

I can't imagine calling her anything else. It's always Iggy and me now.

Iggy's hair

Iggy and me started off with exactly the same hair. Mum says when I was born I had hair like fluff, all soft and sort of see-through.

"You mean bald," Dad says.

"No," Mum says, "It was lovely."

Then it grew and grew, and when I was the age that Iggy is now, it was long and fine and blonde. "Never," says Dad, but it's true. I've seen the pictures.

When Iggy was born, she had see-through

fluff too. Then she grew and her hair grew too, long and fine and blonde. My hair isn't long and fine and blonde any more. My hair is shorter and darker and nothing-er than Iggy's. And my fringe gets in my eyes and it's itchy. So I trimmed it.

I did a really good job. I did it with the kitchen scissors, and I put all the hair in my bin and I put the scissors on my bedside table.

When I went down to the kitchen, Dad didn't even notice. I had to tell him.

"Do you notice anything different about me?" I said.

Dad said, "You're fluent in Japanese."

"No."

"You've turned into a sausage dog."

"No, I don't think so."

"You're a fully-trained astronaut."

"No, Dad. I've cut my hair."

Dad was pouring coffee and he stopped moving. Iggy was picking her nose and she stopped moving.

"Where?" Dad said.

And Iggy said, "On her head, silly."

"I can't see it," he said.

"Well, I have," I said.

Just then, Mum came down from my room with a handful of my hair. She had found it in the bin. "Have you cut your hair?" she said, and she sounded cross. I suddenly sort of wished I hadn't.

"Yes," I said.

"Well, you shouldn't," Mum said in a louder voice than normal. "It's not allowed."

Iggy said, "How did you know she did it, Mum? Me and Dad didn't notice."

"I noticed because she left the evidence in her room," Mum said, and showed her the hair from my bin. It was all fluffy and dry in her hands. It didn't look much like my hair at all, more like a guinea pig's really.

"Oh," Iggy said. "Evidence."

"Still," Dad said to me, "you did a pretty good job."

"Don't do it again," Mum said, and she glared at him and then at me.

So I didn't.

But Iggy did.

She found the scissors by my bed. And because she could make snowflakes out of folded bits of old magazine, she thought she could do anything with scissors.

Mum and Dad said it was my fault what happened, and that I shouldn't cut my own fringe, even just a little bit, and I also shouldn't leave scissors lying around in places where Iggies can find them.

I say when you're Iggy's big sister, everything is your fault, even breathing, because even breathing makes Iggy think of something naughty she could do.

It was after lunch and I was doing times tables in my room. I don't like times tables and because I don't like them I have to do them more than someone who does, which doesn't make any sense to me. I have to say them out loud to myself and throw a ball and catch it while I'm saying them. I feel silly doing that all alone in my room, but Mum and Dad say I have to and they test me afterwards, on my tables and on my catching, so I can't really cheat.

Dad was cutting the grass outside and Mum was working in her room with the sign on the door that says, *Be Quiet Your Mother is Thinking*. Maybe if the lawnmower hadn't been on one of us would have noticed how quiet Iggy was being, because Iggy is not normally quiet. As soon as she stops filling the house with noise, you can almost guarantee she is up to no good.

So when Dad finished and I couldn't hear the mower any more, I couldn't hear Iggy either and I knew there was going to be trouble. Maybe Mum couldn't hear her at the same time because she opened her door and said, "Iggy? Where are you?"

And Dad came in from outside and said, "It's a bit quiet in here."

When Iggy came out of her room she acted like nothing had happened. She came past my door, quieter than normal, and I stopped throwing the ball and trying to remember what seven times four was before I caught it.

"Iggy," I said. "What are you doing?"

"Walking," she said.

"No," I said. "I mean what *have* you been doing?"

"Nothing," she said, in her lying voice, which is very easy to recognise because it's not her real voice at all. It's what she thinks people who are telling the truth sound like.

"Come here," I said, and she turned back and put her head in the room.

Her head with practically no hair on it.

"Iggy!" I said. "What have you done?"

"I've cut my hair," she said, smiling.

I put my hand over my mouth, like a shocked person on the telly, and I said, "Mum and Dad are going to *kill* you!"

"They're not allowed," Iggy said.

"You can't stick hair back on, you know," I said.

"I know. I don't want to."

I couldn't believe what I was seeing. I said, "They are going to be so *cross*!"

"No, they're not," Iggy said. "They're not going to notice." And before I could argue or stop her, she smiled and went downstairs. So I followed her. The back of her head was all different patches, like where Mum fixes the holes in my jeans.

When Iggy walked into Mum's room I counted to two and then I heard Mum shriek like there was a spider down her shirt or a mouse in the fridge or something.

"What's happened?" Dad said. He ran past me in the hall and went into the room with Mum and Iggy in it. I counted to two again and then Dad made a noise that was more of a bellow than a shriek. He sounded like a balloon popping in slow motion.

"What did I say?" Mum said. "What did I say this morning about cutting hair?"

"I haven't cut my hair," Iggy said.

Mum and Dad said, "*What?*" at the same

time, like they'd heard her wrong.

"I haven't cut my hair," she said. "You can look at my room if you like."

"We're looking at your head," Dad said.

"There's no hair in my bin," Iggy said.

"There's no hair on your head either," Dad said.

"There's no *evidence*," Iggy said. "Go and see."

Mum wasn't saying anything. I peeped through the crack in the door and she had her hand over her mouth, just like I'd done, and her eyes were watering like when she peels onions. Dad said he didn't need to go and see, because he could see very well from where he was standing.

"Your beautiful golden hair," Mum said.

"You didn't notice Flo's," Iggy said.

"It's not quite the same," Dad said.

Iggy's voice began to go all wobbly. Her words were starting to run into each other, into one long word. You could tell she was going to start crying, any minute.

"You found the hair in Flo's bin," she said. "But there isn't any hair in mine so you aren't supposed to. *Thereisn'tanyevidence*."

Mum and Dad smiled at each other over Iggy's head. But when Iggy looked at them, they looked cross again. "Show me where you put it," Mum said, and she made Iggy go upstairs in front of her.

Dad came too and he winked at me in the

hallway. "You've got to see this, come on," he said. We followed the back of her head up the stairs and into her room.

Iggy's room has floorboards painted white, with a little red rug on top. We couldn't see any hair. It wasn't in the bin and it wasn't in her bed or under the pillows.

"Where's the rest of your hair?" I said.

"It's not here," Iggy whispered. But I saw her eyes look down at the red rug and then I knew.

We lifted it up together and, underneath, Iggy's chopped and golden hair shifted in the breeze like plants at the bottom of the sea, like the very last bit of a princess who was turning invisible. It looked so pretty lying there that Iggy must have missed it, because she burst into tears.

Dad said, "It's a bit late for that, isn't it?"

Mum said, "When you stop crying, I've got something to show you."

I counted in my head to a hundred and Iggy was nearly finished. Her shoulders were still going up and down, but she wasn't filling the room with noise like before.

"Come with me," Mum said.

We went back downstairs to Mum's thinking room and she opened a drawer, looking for something. Iggy was still sniffing. "Here it is," Mum said, and she pulled out a photo which she gave to Iggy.

"Let's see," I said.

It was a little girl about the same age as Iggy.

"That's me," Mum said, and Iggy giggled.

"You look funny," I said.

"I know," Mum said. "I'd just cut my own hair."

Iggy and me looked really closely at our mum when she was little. Her hair was brown like mine. Her fringe went straight across the very top of her forehead and it was really, really short. She looked silly. But seeing your Mum when she is five is a weird and silly thing anyway, it doesn't matter what her hair looks like.

"Let's have a look," Dad said.

"Do I look like that?" said Iggy.

"No," I said, "Yours doesn't look that bad."

"Not from the front anyway," said Dad.

"Good," Iggy said, and Mum laughed.

Iggy said to Mum, "Did you get told off?"

"A bit," Mum said. "And then I got a new hat and some hair clips."

"Can I have some?" Iggy said.

"Tomorrow maybe," Mum said. "We'll see."

"And when did it come back?" Iggy said, reaching up to twirl a strand of Mum's hair, which is long and shiny, with no fringe any more.

"Oh, a few months," Mum said.

"*Months?*" Iggy said. "Months is *ages*."

Mum stroked Iggy's scruffy hair and looked at her old self in the picture. "No it's not," she said. "You'll see. It's no time at all."

Iggy's world

Iggy is really good at pretending. It is her favourite thing to do. She can turn our front room into a water-lit cave or a forest with a mossy floor or an echoey castle, just by thinking. Her eyes go all wide and then she doesn't see the sofa or the rug or the table like I do, she sees other things. And when she tells me what they are, she's so good at it I start to see them too.

Yesterday, when it was too rainy to go outside, I went into our front room and found Iggy walking very slowly on the spot in the middle of the room. She was wearing sunglasses and had a pillowcase tied round her head.

"What are you wearing that for?" I said.

"To protect me from the sun," she said, as if it was obvious.

"What sun?" I said.

Iggy took her sunglasses off and frowned at me. "The *desert* sun," she said. "It's *scorching*." She pointed to the big lamp that lives in the corner of the room. She had it on the brightest it would go and looking at it made me screw up my eyes, the way the real sun does.

"Where are you going?" I said.

Iggy pointed to the curtains. They have green trees on them. "To that *oasis*," she said. "Come on, we've got to make it there before sunset, and she nodded at the lamp like it might go out any minute, suddenly and without warning.

I taught Iggy what an oasis was. And I told her about the word *scorching*. I learned them at school. We have been doing deserts.

"Am I coming too?" I said.

"So *hot*," Iggy said, putting her sunglasses back on, walking in tiny steps across the rug. "I can't go much further. Oh, for a cup of water in this blistering heat."

"I hope it isn't a *mirage*," I said.

"What isn't?"

"The oasis," I said.

Iggy said, "What's a *mirage*?"

I told her that it was a thing you can see that isn't really there, usually in the desert. "It's seeing things," I said, "but not because you're pretending. It's because of the heat."

"Sounds fun to me," Iggy said.

Then I said, "Do you think we're allowed a biscuit when we get there?"

Iggy stamped her foot and frowned at me again, because I wasn't trying hard enough. "There are no *biscuits* in the desert," she said.

She had a point.

"Sorry," I said.

"Help me get my camel up," she said. "He's fallen over."

Iggy's camel was a beanbag with a blanket thrown over it. She nudged it a bit with her foot and said, "It's no good. I think he's given up. We'll have to leave him behind."

"I'm not leaving a camel in the desert," I

said. (I hate cruelty to animals, even pretend ones.) "I'll carry him."

"You can't carry a *camel*," Iggy said.

"You can if it's a baby one," I said, picking the beanbag up easily. It was a big beanbag, but it wasn't heavy. "Let's pretend the oasis is in the kitchen and then we can ask for a biscuit while we're there."

Iggy took the pillowcase off her head and said, "You are always spoiling things," but she came out to the kitchen with me anyway.

Mum wouldn't let us have a biscuit because lunch was ready. It was green soup. Green soup is Mum's favourite way of tricking us into eating vegetables.

While we were trying to work out what it tasted of, and making sure we had exactly the same size bits of bread, Iggy said, "I know, let's…" This is what she always says when she's about to turn the stairs into an avalanche or the bathroom into the land behind the waterfall.

"I know, let's…" she said, and the kitchen became a dungeon where we (the princesses) had been imprisoned forever by the Wicked Queen (Mum) and made to eat green soup.

"Made out of poisoned toads," Mum said, eating hers quite happily. I think Mum actually likes green soup.

No, *you're* eating the poison," Iggy said to Mum. "And *we're* going to escape."

"Not until you've finished," Mum said.

We ate as quick as we could, then Iggy suddenly hid under the table and said, "Psst! Psst! Hide! Don't let the Wicked Queen see you or she'll cook you for *supper*."

There wasn't time for another drink of water or anything.

Mum wasn't being all that Wicked Queeny. She was doing the washing up and listening to the radio, which is quite normal and not what queens are supposed to do when they've got princesses hiding in their kitchen. I thought Iggy was going to say something about Mum not joining in, but instead she said, "*Look* – she's making a spell in the sink! Now's our chance!"

We made a run for it to the kitchen door. I crashed into the back of Iggy because she was having trouble opening it. Mum turned round to see what all the noise was and Iggy screamed, "Don't look at her or you'll be turned to *stone*!"

We got the door open and made it up the

stairs without the Wicked Queen catching us. Then we fell on the floor and laughed and laughed.

Iggy didn't stop giggling until she rolled over and hit her head on our dressing-up box, which is enormous. "Ow," she said. But she didn't cry. She just opened the lid and looked inside.

The box smells funny and is very old because it used to be Mum's when she was little. There's a whole Dalmatian suit in there and a bear and a pirate and swords and things, because Mum had a brother who is our Uncle Pete. There's also a lot of princess dresses.

Iggy put on a pale blue dress made out of

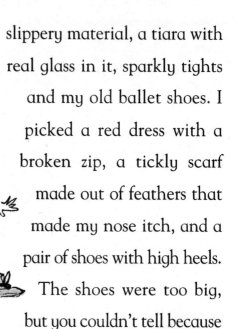

slippery material, a tiara with real glass in it, sparkly tights and my old ballet shoes. I picked a red dress with a broken zip, a tickly scarf made out of feathers that made my nose itch, and a pair of shoes with high heels. The shoes were too big, but you couldn't tell because the dress went all the way down to the floor. They made walking very hard, but it was nice being so tall.

As soon as I was ready to be a princess, Iggy had changed her mind. She said, "I know, let's be pop stars. Let's do a show."

She said, "What's your name going to be?"

"Blanche," I said, because it was the first name that came into my head.

Iggy looked at me funny.

"It's French," I said.

"What does it mean?"

"It means white, I think."

Iggy looked at me even funnier. "Why would anyone want to be called *white?*" she said.

I shrugged my shoulders. "What's *your* name?" I said.

Iggy wasn't wearing the slippery dress any more. She had a black T-shirt on over her sparkly tights, and her sunglasses from the desert. She was pulling faces in the mirror. "My name is *Maddy*," she said in a gravelly

voice. "Out of my way, my fans are waiting."
And she went into my room and put my CD
player on full blast.

"That's too loud," I said, putting the
clothes back in the dressing-up box. Iggy
couldn't hear me. She was jumping around on
my bed, pretending to play the guitar.

"Flo!" Mum said from the bottom of the stairs. "That's too loud!"

"I *know*," I said. "It's not me. It's Iggy."

Mum said. "I'm trying to work."

I turned the music right down.

Iggy stopped jumping around. She picked up my hairbrush and spoke into it like it was a microphone. "Why did you do that?" she said.

"Mum's working," I said.

"So am I," she said.

"You're not really."

Iggy said, "Do you think singing to crowds of people is easy?"

"I don't know," I said. "Shall we do something else?"

I said. "Let's do some drawing. You can stay in my room if you want to do drawing."

"OK," Iggy said.

And we did. Iggy and me sat on my floor and we drew pictures. It was nice and peaceful after so much noisy pretending.

I did a picture of me and Mum and Dad and Iggy in a park with some squirrels and a picnic. Iggy was holding a kite. There was a rainbow. It was one of my best.

"Do you like mine?" Iggy said, and she held it up for me to see. It was an island, with sharks in the water all around, and palm trees and strange birds and snakes and flowers.

"It's really good," I said.

"Thanks," Iggy said, and she drew a big X right in the middle of it. "It's a *treasure map*."

"Wow!"

"Let's do it," she said. "Let's find the treasure right now."

It was still raining. I said, "I don't think we can."

"I hate wet days," Iggy said, looking out of my window in a gloomy way. "The pirates will find all the treasure before we do and there'll be nothing left for us. I'm so *bored* of rain."

She looked so unhappy standing there. I had an idea. "But what if the treasure's not buried outside?" I said.

"What? Where is it?"

"Stay there," I said. "And no peeking."

I went down to Mum and I begged her for some of the biscuits wrapped in shiny paper that she keeps in a very high cupboard. I put them in one of Dad's socks with some marbles and the shiniest bits of rock from my rock collection. And then I hid the sock in the bathroom, in a box Mum keeps our hair brushes in, under a pile of towels.

When I got back to Iggy she was still being gloomy at the window. "Quick," I said. "We have to go now or we've lost our chance."

"Why?" said Iggy, dangling her map in one hand. "Where are we going?"

"It's a trick map," I said. "I heard the pirates talking about it."

"*Really?*"

"Really."

"What's the trick?"

"It's not an island in the sea at all, it just looks like one. It's a special code and I can read it. The treasure is buried inside the pirate's castle. I'll take you to it."

"How do we get there?" Iggy said.

"We have to row across a lake."

"A lake?" she said. "Is it deep?"

"Yes, *really* deep," I said, " and the boat will probably get a hole in it, and there will be crocodiles."

"Oh good," Iggy said, grinning at me. "I *love* crocodiles. Let's go."

And in my suitcase I put...

We were going away to see our friends for the weekend. They are a family just like us, with a mum and a dad and two sisters. They used to live in our street, but now Dad says they live in the middle of nowhere and we have a really long journey to go and see them.

I like going places in our car. It's nice being all together like that. It's not very big and we always take loads of stuff with us so it's really cosy.

Dad says it's not cosy, it's crowded. He says
Mum doesn't need to take thirteen outfits for
three days. He says there's no reason why we
have to bring absolutely all of our toys with
us. He says, "And why do you need to make
exact replicas of your beds in the back?"

"It's comfy," we say.

And he says, "Not with that Sylvanian house digging into the back of my chair, it's not."

It took us quite a long time to get going.

We were all in and Mum had checked our seatbelts. Iggy and me had our pillows in the right place and we were sharing the covers exactly in half. Then we all had to open and shut our doors again, because the light that says one of them is open kept flashing. It's Iggy's door usually. This time it was Mum's.

Then Dad said, "Are we ready?" and Iggy said, "I need a wee."

Mum said, "Oh, Iggy, I asked you that two minutes ago in the house."

"I didn't need one then, " Iggy said, "but now I'm *busting*."

So Dad groaned, and Mum got Iggy out of the car and unlocked the front door and went back inside the house and took her to the loo.

When they came back out, Mum said, "Are you sure you don't need one, Flo?" And even though I'd just been, this little seed of worry got planted in my brain that I might need one in a minute, so I got out and went too.

"*Women!*" Dad said, and Mum said loudly, "We'll ignore that."

Anyway, we all got strapped in again and then we were off. I turned round and looked out of the back window while we drove away from our house. It's fun seeing where you've been.

We didn't get very far because we had to stop at the petrol station and put air in the tyres and buy newspapers and things like that. Iggy wanted crisps.

"You've just had breakfast,' Mum said.

"Can I have cheese and onion?" Iggy said.

"Crisps are bad for you, Iggy," Dad said. "They're full of salt and fat and they give you spots."

"No they don't," Iggy said. "I'm hungry."

Mum rustled around in a bag at her feet and pulled out a banana. "If you're hungry you can have this," she said. "A nice piece of fruit."

"I'm not hungry any more," Iggy said. "I'm thirsty. Can I have a drink?"

"No liquids," Dad said. "Not until we get there. I'm not stopping every five minutes for you to wee."

"I'll hold it in," Iggy said.

"No you won't," said Dad. "That's the problem."

And then we were actually moving.

I watched the people outside on the pavement as we zoomed past them and I wondered if they were going somewhere nice like we were. Maybe to the beach or to visit their granny or have a big lunch with loads of people in their family they hardly know, or to the middle of nowhere, just like us.

On the way we played some games. First we played I Spy. This didn't take very long because Iggy wasn't very good at it. She said, "I spy with my little eye something beginning with tree."

I said, "Tree?" and she said, "Your turn."

I said, "I spy with my little eye something beginning with W."

"Windscreen," Dad said.

I said, "How do you know?"

Mum laughed and said, "You always start with *windscreen*. Just like in Hangman you always start with *elephant*."

This is true, because they are both pretty long words and I never think anyone is going to get them. But they always do.

Then Mum and Dad chose things that were really hard, like N for nothing and G for gearstick, and we gave up.

Next we played Who's in the Bag? I like this game a lot. There's no bag, you just think of a name in your head, like a famous person or a cartoon character, or a piece of fruit (if you're Iggy) and everyone has to guess it. They can ask you questions and you're only allowed to say *Yes* or *No*.

Iggy didn't play it properly. When it was her turn to think of something, I said, "Is it a girl?"

Instead of saying yes or no, she said, "Lemons can't be girls, silly."

So I said, "Is it a lemon?" and she said, "No."

She was cheating.

On her next go, I said, "Is it an animal? (yes) Is it black and white? (yes) Is it a zebra?"

And then all of a sudden it wasn't an animal at all, it was Bart Simpson and then a tangerine. I got cross and then I got in trouble.

Dad said, "Seeing as we're all hurtling along in this metal box on wheels, with no means of escape for the next two and a half hours, do you think you could keep the noise down?"

And Mum said, "I wasn't shouting."

And he said, "I didn't say you were."

Except she was, sort of.

When I wasn't cross with Iggy any more we played the Alphabet Game. You have to go through the whole alphabet the right way round and take it in turns to say boys' names and girls' names. Dad kept saying silly ones.

I said, "Adam."

Iggy said, "Ben."

Mum said, "Chris."

Dad said, "Desmondo."

I said, "Eddie."

Iggy said, "Freddie."

Mum said, "George." (Which Iggy found hysterical for some reason.)

Dad said, "Humperdink." (Which set her off again.)

"Dad!" I said.

He said sorry, but he didn't mean it. He said Lego, Pinky, Taleggio and Xylophone after that, and that was just the boys.

And then Mum said, "Let's play 'I Went on Holiday and in My Suitcase I put…'"

"What's it called?" I said.

"*I Went on Holiday and in My Suitcase I put…*"

"Wow," I said. "That sounds complicated."

"It's fun," Mum said, and she told us how.

It's a game with the longest name in the world probably and it's really good. And we got a big surprise when we played it.

Mum started off and she said, "I went on holiday and in my suitcase I put some pyjamas."

And the next person (which was me) had to say, "I went on holiday and in my suitcase I put some pyjamas… and a book."

And then the next person, who was Iggy, had to remember the pyjamas and the book and added a sunhat.

And then the next person, who was Dad, had to remember the pyjamas and the book and the sunhat and then said, "A loo brush." Which was very silly.

The game went on and on, and

the list got longer, and the suitcase got bigger and fuller, and we had to think really hard to remember all the stuff we'd packed in just the right order. I think I remembered about eight or twelve things, and then I got a bit tied up in knots and my brain ached and I had to stop.

I don't know how many things Iggy remembered. I lost count. She was sitting next to me in her booster seat with way more than half the covers on her.

She said, "I went on holiday and in my suitcase I put some pyjamas, a book, a sunhat, a loo brush, some sandals, some sun cream, my teddy,

an armadillo, my alarm clock, my camera, a mobile phone, some eggs, a map, some sunglasses, a pencil case, some kippers and... a bikini."

"That's seventeen," Mum said to Dad. "That's amazing." We all had our mouths open at how good Iggy was at the game.

Dad said to Iggy, "You have a remarkable memory."

"What does that mean?" said Iggy.

"I can't remember," said Dad.

"It means very, very good indeed," said Mum.

"What about me?" I said.

"Yours is very good too, sieve brain," said Dad. (I know he was only joking because he winked at me in his special mirror.)

"Can we play again?" Iggy said.

So we did. Three more times. Iggy's memory was remarkable every time.

We played it all the way until we arrived in the middle of nowhere. Suddenly there we were, in no time at all, and our friends were running down the path to meet us and show us the swing in their garden and where we were going to sleep.

"Hello," we all said to each other, apart from Iggy.

Iggy wasn't getting out of the car, which was strange, because she loves swings in gardens, and she especially loves our friends and she'd been excited about visiting for ages.

"Come on, Iggy," said Dad. "Out you get."

"What's the matter, Iggy?" Mum said.

"Can you only play it in a car?" Iggy said.

"Play what?" we said.

"I went on holiday and in my suitcase I put…" Iggy said.

Mum and Dad laughed.

"No, Iggy," I said, and I held out my hand so she could hold it. "You can play it in gardens and on swings and in other people's houses and anywhere in the whole world you feel like playing it."

"Good," Iggy said. "Let's go and teach the others."

Iggy and the babysitter

Mum and Dad were going out and we needed a babysitter.

"What's a babysitter?" Iggy said.

"It's a person who squashes naughty children," said Dad, and Mum told him off.

"No it's not," she said. "It's a person who looks after you when we go out."

"Go out where?" Iggy said.

"Exactly," Dad said. "When do we ever go out?"

"Next Friday," Mum said. "We're going to the theatre, remember? It's been booked for ages. And for supper at the French place."

"What supper do you get there?" Iggy said, like she wanted to go with them.

"Snails," Dad said, pulling a face, and Iggy stopped wanting straightaway.

"What about Granny and Grandpa?" I said. "They're good at looking after us." Granny and Grandpa are Mum's mum and dad. Sometimes we go and stay with them on our own. They live very far away and they have two cats and a big tin that's only for chocolate.

"They're on holiday," Mum said.

"Get Rwaida," Iggy said. Rwaida is Iggy's teacher at school.

Mum said, "She spends all day looking after you. She's not going to want to come and do it at night too."

"She might," Iggy said.

"She's a qualified teacher," Mum said. "Qualified teachers don't do babysitting."

I said that Granny was a qualified teacher too, because she used to be, and Grandpa used to know how to fly a real plane, and they both did babysitting.

Mum said, "That's not the point, Miss Smartypants. They do it for free."

"What about Auntie Kate?" Iggy said.

"Auntie Kate lives in America," I told her.

"So?" Iggy said. "Can't she come over just for one night?"

"No," Mum said.

"That's not fair," Iggy said.

"Life's not fair," Mum said, and Iggy said, "Why not?" and Mum didn't answer.

"Can't we go and stay somewhere?" I said. "We could go to Star's house."

Star is my absolute best friend and she lives over the road from me at number twenty-nine. I've stayed there about thirty-three times.

Iggy's eyes went all sparkly and excited. "We could have a *sleepover*," she said.

"I don't think so," Mum said.

Iggy's never stayed at a friend's house. This is because she is very little and also because sometimes she wets the bed, but I'm not supposed to know because it's private and a secret.

"What about Mrs Butler?" I said.

Mrs Butler lives next door. She wears a purple hat and tights the colour her legs would go if she went on holiday and got a tan. Her face is very pale under her purple hat and her legs are very brown. I don't know what colour her hair is because I've never seen it. She always says, "Hello, girls," when we see her in the street, and one Saturday she gave me 10p for sweets without me even asking. This is why I thought she might make a good babysitter.

"I don't think Mrs Butler will get up these stairs," Mum said, "let alone chase you two around for hours."

"Why will we be running?" Iggy said, with a face that tried to say she never darts about like a squealing mouse, or dances on the table, or jumps up and down on the sofa while people are trying to read.

"Who, me?" her face said.

"Yes, you," said Mum's face.

In the end, Mum found a lady called Joanna, who was the daughter of her friend at yoga or something like that. Mum spoke to her on the phone and the week before Mum and Dad were going out, she came round to meet us. She had purple hair. And black painted fingernails. And an earring in her eyebrow. You could see that she was really pretty underneath.

"Do we have to stay home alone with *her?*" Iggy said while we stood on the doormat, waiting to meet her.

"*Sssh!*" Mum said. "And yes, you do."

"Hello," Joanna said, and I said, "Hello," but Iggy hid behind my back and wouldn't come out.

"She's shy," I said, and Dad snorted because shy is the very last thing that Iggy is. I frowned at him for giving the game away. "She *is*," I said.

"No, I'm not," Iggy said. "I just don't like purple hair."

"Iggy!" Mum said. "That's very rude."

"It's OK," Joanna said, and when Iggy peeped out at her she smiled. "You don't have to like purple hair. I don't mind."

The night that Mum and Dad were going out, Joanna came round to babysit. She was carrying a big bag of something and this time her hair was orange. Iggy's mouth dropped open like a trapdoor and she hid behind me again. My pyjama top was all squished up in her fists and her nose pressed into my back.

"Come out, Iggy," I said, trying to get her off me, but she wouldn't. I tried to smile at Joanna at the same time, but it was quite hard. It came out more like pulling a face.

"I like your hair," Mum said.

"I thought Iggy might prefer it orange,"
Joanna said.

I could feel Iggy shaking her head against
me. I smiled even harder.

Mum was all dressed up and she looked really different in a good way, and Dad was wearing a suit.

"My mum and dad are going to eat snails," I said. "Have you eaten a snail?"

"No," Joanna said. "I'm a vegan."

"What's that?" I said. I wondered if it had something to do with the colour of her hair.

Mum said it meant that Joanna didn't eat any meat or fish or eggs or milk or anything at all that came from animals.

"Iggy's nearly one of those," I said. "All she wants to eat is Rice Crispies."

When we said goodbye to Mum and Dad, I had to help tickle Iggy to get her to unlock her arms from Mum's neck. Mum left lots of phone numbers in case of emergency. I wondered what emergencies she was thinking might happen and I was a bit worried about it, but I didn't have time to ask.

After they'd gone it was quiet for a minute. Iggy held on to my hand and she wouldn't let go. Then Joanna said, "OK, who wants to do some art with me?" and she walked into the kitchen with her big bag, like she was expecting us to follow her.

I looked at Iggy and she looked at me. She

pulled this face, with her eyebrows up really high and her bottom lip stuck out really far, and she shrugged her shoulders.

"What sort of art?" I said. I really like drawing so I was already going to say yes.

"Really good fun art,' Joanna said, and she came out of the kitchen with a big roll of paper in her hand.

"What's that?" I said.

"It's wallpaper," she said. "For drawing on."

Iggy said, "We're not allowed to draw on

the walls. We get in very big trouble when we do that."

Joanna laughed. She said, "It's not going on the walls, it's going on the floor."

Iggy shook her head. "We can't draw on the floor either," and she rolled her eyes at me as if she was saying, "Doesn't this babysitter know *anything*?"

"Don't worry," Joanna said. "We're not drawing on anything we're not supposed to. Come in here and lie down."

"Lie down?" I said.

Iggy and me looked at each other again. Iggy said, "I don't want to."

"Come on, Iggy," I said. "It'll be fun. Let's go."

Iggy took tiny steps on our way to the

kitchen. It took quite a long time to get there.

"Who wants to go first?" Joanna said, and Iggy pushed me in the back, which was her way of saying that I did.

"I do," I said.

Joanna unrolled the big roll of paper out on the floor and put a book at each end to stop it from curling back up again. "On you get," she said. "Lie down on that."

"Really?" I said.

"Yep. That's it."

I lay down on the paper and looked up at her. The floor was cold and bony. If I turned my head to the side I could see *loads* of fluff under the cooker. Iggy looked really worried again.

"Are you good at art?" I said to Joanna.

"I'm all right," she said. "Now hold still."

"What are you going to do?" I said.

"I'm not going to do anything," she said.
"Iggy is. Come on, Iggy."

Iggy was lurking in the doorway with her
thumb in her mouth and Joanna held out a
pen to her. A big, fat, smelly, red one that
made Iggy's thumb pop out and her feet start
moving across the floor. I noticed she didn't
have any slippers on. Mum would've had
something to say about that, but Joanna
didn't seem to mind.

"Draw round your sister," she said.

"All round?" Iggy said.

"Yep," said Joanna. "Just like you draw
round your hand on a piece of paper."

So Iggy took the lid off the pen and got down really low so her face was really close to mine. "Stay still," she said, and she started to draw, climbing around me while she did it. The pen made a funny noise through the floor and into my ears while she went round me, now above my head, now round my fingers, now by my knee, now at my feet. When I got up, there I was still lying on the paper, a bit wobbly in places, but the same size as real life. I was quite surprised by how big I am.

Joanna was pulling things out of her bag – material and paper and glue and pencils and glitter and stuff. "We've got to get her dressed now," she said.

So we started cutting and sticking, and soon the girl who wasn't me, but was exactly my size, was wearing a skirt and a T-shirt and a cardigan and stripy socks and big glittery shoes.

After that I drew round Iggy, and then we both drew round Joanna who was nearly as tall as Iggy and me put together.

When it was time to go to bed, we helped Joanna tidy up, and then she helped us clean our teeth and wash our faces.

Iggy took the picture of Joanna in her room because she said it would be like having a babysitter there all the time, and she would sleep really well and not get up once.

"Goodnight," Joanna said. "Sleep tight."

"Goodnight," I said.

"Goodnight," Iggy said.

And then she said, "Joanna."

And Joanna said, "Yes?"

"I like purple hair really," said Iggy. "And orange hair too. I like it a lot."

Doctor Iggy

One day, Iggy woke up and decided to be a doctor. Not a doctor for people, but a doctor for toys.

It started at our school fair. That's where Iggy got her first sick toy. It was a little elephant that could fit in her hand. It had a squashed trunk and a missing leg. It looked very sorry for itself indeed. Iggy asked me for 5p so she could buy it.

All the way back she held the elephant in

both hands really gently, as if it might break.

"Is it a boy or a girl?" I said.

"I don't know," Iggy said, not taking her eyes off it. "I haven't looked yet."

"Watch where you're going," Mum said to her. "You'll bump into people."

When we got home, Iggy took the sick elephant straight upstairs. She put on a doctor's coat, which was actually the top half of my judo suit. It's a bit big even for me and it came all the way down to her ankles. She put on the black plastic glasses that used to have a false nose before she pulled it off. She rushed around upstairs looking for Post-it notes and Sellotape, and in the bathroom she filled a little cup from her teaset with water.

When she had everything she needed, she looked at the elephant all over with a magnifying glass. She poked it with a cotton bud. She said, "Where does it hurt?" and "You're being very brave," and "What a good patient," just like a real doctor.

She decided what was wrong with it – a broken leg (obviously) and a very bad cold. Then she cured it with a dab of water and a bandage made of loo roll. She wet the elephant's trunk and wrapped it up, and she did the same to the place where its leg should be. Then she made a bed for it on the floor, out of a shoebox and a pillow from my doll's pram.

Ever since then Iggy has collected toys that have something wrong with them. If she finds a bear with one eye, or a dog with no tail, or a squirrel with a stuffing problem, Iggy has to take it home. If we leave it behind she worries and worries. I think Iggy really cares about sick toys. And Mum says that 20p here and there is worth it for the peace and quiet.

Iggy's room has a bed with a table next to it, and a tall cupboard to put all her clothes in. That's it. Iggy's room isn't very big. And because of all the sick toys and the bandages and everything, Iggy's room is overcrowded.

"Just like a real hospital," Dad said.

Iggy arranges all her patients in straight rows, like in a ward. She makes beds for them out of all the clothes that should be in her tall cupboard. Sometimes she's got no clean T-shirts because there's a bandaged toy on every single one of them. Sometimes you can't even get to her bed, the floor is so covered with sleeping toys. And if you even

just *nearly* tread on one, you are in trouble with Iggy for days.

"This healthcare business is getting out of hand," Dad said, trying to put Iggy to bed with only one foot on the floor.

"What is?" said Iggy.

While Dad was balancing, I closed my eyes because I thought he was about to land on a kangaroo with a torn pouch.

"This hospital," he said. "It's *everywhere*."

"I know," said Iggy.

"Can't you move them over a bit?" I said.

I was only trying to be helpful, but Iggy glared at me. "They'll get squashed," she said.

Dad said that by the look of some of

them, "squashed" was what they did for a living.

"It's not funny, Daddy," Iggy said, and you could tell from her frown and her pointing finger that she was deadly serious. "Some of these teddies are very not happy," she said. "And I am all they've got."

Just when she said that, a big pile of jumpers fell out of the tall cupboard with a *thwump*. Dad looked at Iggy, and he looked at the jumpers (which had somehow landed between the doll with one eye and a pair of earless teddies), and then he looked at me. "I think this house is sinking," he said. "We must be on a slope."

"What *are* you talking about?" Mum said, trying to find somewhere to stand as she came in the room. It was her turn to read to Iggy and my turn to read with Dad.

"The house is sinking," I said.

"Dad wants to shrink my hospital," Iggy said.

Mum looked at Dad and he held his hands

out, like a teapot with two spouts and no handle. "What?" he said. "It's a mess in here. You can't see the floor."

Mum pointed her finger at Dad, just like Iggy did, and she said, "Saving lives is a messy business."

"True," Dad said.

"And the house is *not* sinking," she said. "Please tell the girls the house isn't sinking."

Dad said to us, "The house is not sinking," and he said it in a voice like Iggy's when she's been naughty and she has to say sorry. Then he said to Mum, "So why are the clothes forever falling out of the cupboard?"

"I don't know," said Mum. "Maybe because it's not meant for clothes. And the doctor here isn't the world's best at folding."

Me and Dad went to my room to read a book. My room is bigger than Iggy's. I don't have as many toys and my clothes live in an ordinary chest of drawers. Dad says it doesn't look like it's in the same house.

It was my turn to read a page. That's what we do at bedtime – we take it in turns to read the book. When it was Dad's page I couldn't really listen because I was having an idea. It's very hard to listen to someone else reading when you are having one of those.

Dad said, "Are you listening?"

"Sorry," I said. "I was thinking."

"What about?"

"Iggy's cupboard," I said.

Dad said he was only joking about the house sinking.

"I know," I said. "I wasn't thinking about that. I was thinking her cupboard would make a really good Toy Hospital."

On Saturday morning, Mum said she was taking Iggy out to get her some drawers that the clothes didn't fall out of.

"What am I doing?" I said.

"You are going to be busy," Dad said, and he winked at me.

Iggy said, "Doing what?"

"Putting out the rubbish," Dad said, which

is Iggy's idea of the worst job ever, so she didn't ask any more.

"What are we really doing?" I said to Dad when they were gone.

"I'm really putting out the rubbish," Dad said. "You're going to make a Toy Hospital."

First, I pulled all the clothes out of Iggy's cupboard and put them sort of in piles on her bed.

Then I measured the shelves, which was very tricky because the ruler was too short. I cut out some paper nearly the right size and I drew loads of beds on it, all around the edges, with a pencil. I coloured in all the bedspreads, and I drew pillows and bedside tables and everything.

It was one of my best drawings ever. I had to do it four times because there were four shelves, and my hand was aching and aching when I finished. Some of the beds had to be much bigger than others because so were some of the sick teddies.

Then I put the paper in the right place and

I picked up all the sick toys, one by one, and put them to bed in the cupboard. And I picked up all the clothes they'd been lying on and made a sort of pile of them on the bed too.

"How are you getting on?" said Dad, coming into the room. I was very busy and concentrating and he made me jump.

We stepped back and had a look. The cupboard looked like a real hospital. I almost wished it was mine.

"It's brilliant," Dad said. "Well done, Flo."

I was really excited for Iggy to get home.

Dad got the little stepladder from the kitchen so that she would be able to visit the ward on the top floor. "Look!" he said. It sounded really urgent.

"What?" I said.

He was standing in the middle of Iggy's room, looking down.

"You can see the floor," he said. "It's a miracle!"

When Iggy came back with Mum and a chest of drawers, I was waiting with her doctor's coat, all ready at the bottom of the stairs. I wanted her to put it on before she went up to her room.

"What happened?" she said. "Who got sick?"

"Nobody," Dad said. "You just got a huge amount of funding."

"What's that mean?" Iggy said

We waited for Iggy and Mum to go upstairs and see before we answered.

"Flo built you a hospital," Dad said, and he mussed up my hair while he was saying it.

Iggy's eyes went all round and her mouth was round too, and she said, "That. Is. The. Best. Hospital. Ever."

"It's multi-storey," I said.

"Look at the *beds*!" she said. "They look real."

"I did those," I said.

Iggy climbed the stepladder and inspected her new hospital. She was smiling and I think she really liked it.

But then she said, "Uh-oh."

And I said, "What's wrong?" I couldn't think of anything I'd left out.

Iggy looked at each floor of the hospital one more time. "The beds are all full," she said.

Dad said, "Is that a problem?"

Iggy looked at Mum, and Mum looked at me and Dad. Then Iggy held out her hand and Mum gave her a plastic bag.

"Well," Iggy said, "there was a table with some teddies on it."

"Oh no!" Dad said.

Iggy tipped the bag out on to the floor. Three toys fell out – a bald seahorse, a cat with no nose and a snake whose tongue was hanging off in one long thread.

"Oh no!" he said again.

"It's OK," Iggy said, choosing three T-shirts from the pile on the bed. "I can start again on the floor."

Goodnight, Iggy

The other night, because supper wasn't ready yet and we had run out of other things to do, Mum said we could watch a film. She sent us into the telly room to choose. This can be very hard because Iggy and me don't always agree. Sometimes choosing the same DVD to watch takes nearly as long as watching it.

"I want to watch this one," Iggy said. It had a picture of a cowboy on it. He looked uncomfortable.

"That's an 18," I said. "We can't watch that."

"Why not?" Iggy said.

"Because we are not *eighteen*," I told her.

"Nor is Dad," she said. "*He* watches it."

"He is *more* than eighteen," I said. "That doesn't count."

"What about this one?" Iggy said. I don't know why she picked it up. It's for babies.

"No way," I said. "You've seen that a hundred times. We're not watching it again."

We rummaged around a bit more. "Here's one," I said. "It's about mermaids. It's so good."

"*Boring*," Iggy said.

I was beginning to lose hope.

"What's this?" Iggy said.

It had a boy on it dressed in black with funny teeth and little glasses. It looked good. It wasn't an 18. We hadn't seen it before.

"OK," I said. Let's show Mum."

Mum was in the kitchen making steam everywhere. I think we were having pasta. Pasta is Mum's favourite thing to cook. She is *always* cooking it.

"I don't think you'll like it," Mum said, looking at the DVD through a steam cloud.

"Why not?" I said.

"*You'd* be OK with it, Flo," she said. "I just think it might be too much for Iggy."

Iggy didn't like the sound of that one bit. "Why?" she said.

"It's a bit scary," Mum said.

"I won't be scared," Iggy said.

"I'm not sure," Mum said. "I don't think so."

So we went back to try and choose something different. Except Iggy had made her mind up. Every time I showed her a DVD she just shut her eyes and shook her head. "Nope," she said. "I want this one." And she didn't let go of the scary film with the boy on the front.

In the end, Mum came in to see how we were doing.

"We can't find one," I said. "I think we give up."

"Because *you* won't let us watch the one we want," Iggy said.

Mum said, "Well, I don't want you to be scared."

"Oh, *please*," Iggy said. "I won't be anything, I promise."

Mum did some thinking for a bit.

She said, "OK. Give it a try. But turn it off if you don't like it."

The film was about a boy in a castle. When he was asleep in the middle of the night, another boy flew in through his window. The flying boy was the one with funny teeth. He was a vampire. He was just trying to make friends.

"I don't like this film," Iggy said.

"I do," I said.

"I *really* don't," said Iggy, and she meant it, so we turned it off and played cards instead.

Iggy was very quiet when we were eating our supper. She was very quiet in the bath, and she was very quiet after Mum and Dad said goodnight and went downstairs. Normally when they go, she starts calling me through the wall, or rings the doorbell that starts in her room and ends in mine, or starts singing loud enough for me to have to ask her to be quiet.

This time there was nothing. No Iggy noise at all.

I lay in my bed and I thought about the boy in the castle lying in his. The windows in his room were all noisy and rattly, and the curtains kept moving and there were trees outside knocking like they wanted to come in. My window was quiet and there was a streetlight outside and my curtains were well behaved and still. I was glad I didn't live in a castle in a film like that.

The next thing I knew, Iggy woke me up. She was standing by my bed and tapping me.

"What?" I said.

"I can't sleep," Iggy said.

"Why not?" I said.

"I'm the only person awake in the whole world."

"No you're not," I said. "I'm awake too. What's wrong?"

Iggy didn't say anything.

"What's the matter?" I said.

"I'm scared," she said.

"Of what?"

"Of the boy who flies into rooms." Iggy gave herself a hug when she said that, like she was very, very cold.

"He won't fly into your room," I said.

"How do *you* know?"

"Because it's just a film," I said.

"I didn't like it."

"But it wasn't real," I said. "It was just pretend."

Iggy looked at me. "I *still* didn't like it," she said. "And it's not letting me sleep."

She stood at the side of my bed waiting for me to do something. I didn't know what the thing was.

"Did you go and see Mum and Dad?" I said. Iggy shook her head. "Why not?"

She shrugged her shoulders. "Don't know."

I said, "Is it because the film made you scared?"

Iggy shrugged again. "Don't know," she said.

I said, "Is it because Mum won't let you watch a film for *ages* if she finds out?"

Iggy frowned at me. "Don't know," she said. But she did.

I said, "Do you want to get in with me?"

She nodded. I moved over in my bed and lifted the covers for her. Iggy's feet were really cold.

"Don't touch me," I said.

"Why not?"

"Your feet are like ice."

Iggy giggled. She put her feet on me again.

"*Don't*, Iggy," I said. She giggled again. "If you do it again," I said, "you have to go back to your own bed."

"Sorry," she said. "Don't make me do that. I was just awake in there."

"I thought you went to sleep straightaway,"

I said. "You were really quiet."

"I know," she said. "I didn't want the boy to hear me. I had to lie really still and I didn't even blink or anything."

"Did you fall asleep?" I said.

"I don't know," she said. "I was keeping watch."

I made sure the covers were on both of us and I closed my eyes. "I'll keep watch now," I said.

"OK."

It was quiet, but not for long.

"Flo," Iggy said.

"Yes."

"Do they still have castles, in the real world?"

"I think so," I said.

"Oh."

I closed my eyes again.

"Do people live in them?"

"I think so. Sometimes."

"Who?"

"Rich people and kings and stuff."

"Are the castles just like in the film?" Iggy said.

"I don't know," I said. "Like what?"

"Like haunted and candles and scary music," she said.

I thought about the castle in the DVD. It was full of dark corridors and gloomy paintings and everything was dusty. There were bound to be bats. And mice. And ghosts.

I began to wish I hadn't watched the film either. "Go to sleep Iggy," I said.

"What if the boy flies in through your window," she said. "What will we do?"

"He won't," I said.

"Are you sure?"

"I think so," I said.

"OK," she said, and she turned over and took all the covers with her.

I looked at my window and I thought about the flying boy. He only wanted to make friends. It must be hard having friends when everyone is scared of you.

"I wonder what happened," Iggy said.

"When?"

"In the film," she said. "I want to know what happens next."

"Me too."

"Shall we watch some more?"

"Mum won't let you," I said.

"Yes she will."

"What if it's even scarier?" I said. "What will you do then?"

"I'll come in and look after you," Iggy said. And she giggled, and put her not-so-cold feet on me again.

"'Night, Flo," she said.

"Goodnight, Iggy," I said.

And soon she was asleep. Iggy snores. She snores like a little hippo.

I know because I was keeping watch.

A new house

Mum and Dad said we had to move house.

Iggy said, "Where are we going to put it?" And so they had to explain that we weren't moving our house somewhere else, we were leaving it where it was and moving to a different one.

Iggy and me didn't want to. We liked our house a lot. It had a garden with real grass and a blue front door of its own and our bedrooms were full of nice things.

Mum said, "We have to move. This place is getting too small for us."

"It's not too small," I said. "It's cosy."

Dad laughed. "Cosy? You can't swing a cat in here."

"So don't then," I said. "You shouldn't anyway."

"Why do we have to move?" Iggy said.

"It's because of you," Dad said to us. "You won't stop growing."

He said, "We keep telling you to stop growing, but you don't listen. It's very hard work living with people who get bigger all the time."

Iggy looked at Dad like she was working out something she didn't know before.

"Aren't *you* growing?" she said.

Dad shook his head. "Not me," he said "Your mum and I stopped growing a long time ago."

"Then who lets you have new shoes?" she said. "We only get new shoes when we're growed out of the old ones."

"Ah!" Dad said, "Clever," and he tapped his head with two fingers. Then he said, "When you leave home you get a special note from your mum and dad that says you're allowed to buy new shoes and books and bicycles and houses and things, as long as you are very sensible."

"No you don't," I said. "That's silly."

"It's not silly," he said. "It's true."

"I don't believe you," I said.

"Oh, so you won't be needing a note when you leave home," he said.

"I will," said Iggy.

I said to Mum, "Are we buying a new house, really?" and she said we were.

Iggy and me looked at each other and our mouths dropped open and we didn't know what to think.

"It'll be fun," Dad said. "Sort of. You wait and see."

I didn't know what *sort of* was supposed to mean, and I didn't see how it could be fun leaving everything behind and going somewhere you hadn't even seen before. I said so. Mum and Dad said we shouldn't worry too much and it was all going to be fine, and if we had any questions we should ask.

So we did.

We chased them from room to room with questions. Like did we have to move schools? And did we have time to warn our friends? And could we take our stuff with us? And how were we supposed to carry it all? And how would we find our way home when we didn't know where it was? And what if we left something behind that was hidden and we'd forgotten about it and we only remembered it after we moved? And who was getting our house anyway?

Dad said we were moving house, not emigrating. I didn't know what this meant.

Mum said we could stay at the same school and keep the same friends and take everything we wanted with us, within reason. I didn't know what that meant either.

Dad said, "It means moving to the other side of the world. We're not doing that."

Mum said, "It means you can't take sweet wrappers and odd socks and old half-eaten biscuits."

"Who would want to?" Iggy said.

Mum said she had some pictures of the new house that was still somebody else's old house with all their stuff in it. "That's your room, Iggy," she said, and she pointed to a picture with an armchair and a giant pair of curtains.

Iggy shuddered and put her thumb in her mouth.

"And that's yours, Flo," she said, and she pointed to a different picture with a bed and a scary wardrobe and more giant curtains.

"Oh," I said, and Iggy said, "That room looks bigger than mine."

"It is bigger," Mum said.

"Huh?" said Iggy, which was a quick way of saying, "How come?" and "That's not fair," at the same time.

Mum said that I was the oldest so I was having the big room, end of story.

Iggy scowled at me and said that when she grew up and got older than me, she was going to have the big room.

Dad said, "When you're older than Flo you can." And then he winked at me, because Iggy didn't know she'd never be older than me, but we did.

After that it was ages before we moved. I kept hoping that Mum and Dad had forgotten about it.

Once we went to see the new house. It didn't seem to belong to anybody and it was a bit smelly, and the giant curtains from the photos looked like there were burglars hiding in them. But the garden was nice. Dad said we could have a slide and a sandpit, and then

Iggy wasn't worried about moving any more, it was just me.

And once, the two people who were going live in our house next came to look round. They were called Charlie and Tom and they didn't have any children, but they did have cats. Charlie kept touching things and Tom wanted to look in all the cupboards. I didn't want him to look in mine because it wasn't as tidy as it was supposed to be.

Packing our stuff was really hard because we had to fit every single thing into boxes and not leave anything behind because we weren't ever coming back. Mum gave Iggy

and me four boxes each and we had to fit our whole rooms into them.

First I folded my clothes really small and then I crammed my teddies in so it was a real squish. I had to sit on that box so I could do it up with brown tape. Then I made a pile of things that maybe didn't have to move house with me, like old pictures and lumps of Blu-Tack and some games where most of the pieces had gone missing because Iggy never puts anything away properly ever.

Iggy wasn't very good at fitting her room into four boxes so I had to help her. She said she couldn't put her teddies in a box because they wouldn't be able to see. She said, "How can I put all my clothes in there?

I'll have nothing to wear tomorrow."

And there wasn't one thing she wanted to throw away either, not even screwed up old bits of paper I found under her bed, or a lollipop that had been sitting on the radiator for ages and turned into a pool of stick.

"Mum!" I said. "Iggy won't pack her stuff."

"You do it for her," Dad said. "Iggy, you can come with me and do the recycling."

Iggy couldn't get up fast enough. She loves doing that. She sits on Dad's shoulders and posts the bottles in the holes, and she squeals every time they smash.

"My teddies need windows," she said to me before she left the room. "Don't put them in there. They don't like the dark."

I packed her clothes and her books and her drawings. I found my favourite hairclip in her knicker drawer, and a notebook I thought was lost under her pillow. I packed everything and I put all her teddies on her bed, and then I went to find Mum.

She was wrapping all the plates and cups and glasses in newspaper. The kitchen looked all upside-down and inside-out because the cupboards were empty and everything was everywhere.

Mum kept blowing the hair out of her eyes

with her bottom lip. Her fingers were all inky from the paper. "This," she said, "is such a hassle."

I helped her for a bit. It was quite fun, like presents. We wrapped up everything apart from four plates and four cups and four knives and forks.

"One more meal in this house," Mum said, which made me a bit sad.

Then she said, "It'll have to be a takeaway," which cheered me up again because we hardly ever have those.

She found me a see-through plastic sort of suitcase thing to put Iggy's teddies in. I filled it up and I bumped it back downstairs into the kitchen to show her.

"Bet she makes me cut holes in it," I said, "so they can breathe."

When Dad and Iggy came back, the whole kitchen was in boxes on the floor and Mum had started on the sitting room. I was trying to watch TV and eat a biscuit, but she kept getting in the way.

"Go out and play," Mum said, "or draw a picture or something."

"I've packed all my pens," I said.

"Well, find something to do," she said. "Go and say goodbye to all the cobwebs."

"*Cobwebs?*" Dad said. "Surely not, darling." And she stuck her tongue out at him.

I went upstairs and wandered around because when all the rooms in your house are empty there's a lot less to do. It was strange seeing the shapes on the walls where our pictures used to be. And the place by their bedroom door where Mum and Dad had measured Iggy and me. We'd been in that house since we were so small you could hardly believe.

I could hear Iggy downstairs talking and talking and talking. After a bit more wandering I went to find everyone. Mum was on the sofa. She said, "I can't look at anything that moves without thinking about packing it."

Dad said, "I'll make you a cup of tea."

Mum said, "You can't. I packed the kettle."

I sat on Mum's knee and we stared at where the telly used to be. "This time tomorrow," she said, "you'll be unpacking in your new room."

I thought about the curtains and the

strange bed and the ugly old wardrobe and I tried really hard to smile.

"It'll be fun," Mum said. "You'll see."

We had curry for supper. Iggy and me had rice and lentils and poppadoms, and we tried some of Dad's, which made my eyes water and my mouth be on fire even after I'd gone to bed. My room was really empty. It wasn't like my room at all.

In the morning, four men came from Australia with a big lorry and started putting our boxes in it. It was the biggest lorry I had ever seen and all the things we had packed looked lost inside.

Dad said Iggy and me were getting in the way so Mum took us to the playground near our house, which wasn't going to be so near our house any more after today.

"Will there be a new one?" I said.

"A new what?" Mum asked.

"A new playground near our new house."

"Of course there will," Mum said. "Anyway, this one won't be that far."

After ages and ages Mum's phone rang and it was Dad. We went home to meet him and say goodbye to our house and never come back. The lorry with all our things in had gone.

Our house didn't look like our house any more. It looked like anyone's. It looked like Charlie and Tom's. Mum left them a note and a bottle of milk in the kitchen. It said, "We hope you have a lovely time here. We did."

We got in the car and we drove to our new house. It was surprisingly quick. When we got there, the lorry was already parked outside and the men were carrying our things in.

I went up to the room that was going to be mine. The curtains had gone. There wasn't a big scary wardrobe any more, or a bed, or an armchair. And it was all painted light blue, which is my favourite colour.

While I was standing there noticing, Iggy came rushing in. "Flo!" she said. "I've just seen your bed! It's coming up the stairs!"

We squished ourselves into the corner so we didn't get in the way. The men put my bed down on the floor.

"Where do you want it?" one of them said, and Iggy nudged me for an answer.

I thought for a minute and then I said, "Over there, please," and I pointed at the window.

Iggy's room was painted yellow, which is her favourite colour. I went with her to see because she didn't want to do it on her own. Standing in it was like standing inside sunshine, or an egg. It was bigger than her old room.

Mum and Dad came to find us with our boxes of things. "When you've unpacked your stuff," they said, "it'll feel just like home."

They gave us surprise presents which were signs for our doors. One side said COME IN and the other side said KEEP OUT.

"I like moving house," Iggy said, opening her bag of teddies.

I thought about the boxes in my new room filled with all my old things. I thought about sitting on my bed by my new window and looking out.

"So do I," I said.

The end

About the author

Jenny Valentine moved house every two years when she was growing up. She worked in a wholefood shop in Primrose Hill for fifteen years where she met many extraordinary people and sold more organic loaves than there are words in her first novel, *Finding Violet Park*, which won the Guardian Children's Fiction Prize. *Iggy and Me* is her first book for younger readers, but it won't be her last!

About the illustrator

Joe Berger grew up in Bristol, where he did an Art Foundation Course before moving to London in 1991. He works as a freelance illustrator and animator, and also co-writes and illustrates a weekly comic strip in the *Guardian*. His first picture book, *Bridget Fidget*, was nominated for the Booktrust Early Years Award.

Look out for
more stories about
Iggy and me.

In the next book, we go swimming,

put on a play,

go on a day out,

and Iggy makes a birthday list.